A Note to Parents

DK READERS is a compelling programme for beginning readers, designed in conjunction with leading literacy experts, including Maureen Fernandes, B.Ed (Hons). Maureen has spent many years teaching literacy, both in the classroom and as a consultant in schools.

Beautiful illustrations and superb full-colour photographs combine with engaging, easy-to-read stories to offer a fresh approach to each subject in the series. Each DK READER is guaranteed to capture a child's interest while developing his or her reading skills, general knowledge and love of reading.

The five levels of DK READERS are aimed at different reading abilities, enabling you to choose the books that are exactly right for your child:

Pre-level 1: Learning to read
Level 1: Beginning to read
Level 2: Beginning to read alone
Level 3: Reading alone
Level 4: Proficient readers

The "normal" age at which a child begins to read can be anywhere from three to eight years old. Adult participation through the lower levels is very helpful for providing encouragement, discussing storylines and sounding out unfamiliar words.

No matter which level you select, you can be sure that you are helping your child learn to read, then read to learn!

LONDON, NEW YORK, MUNICH,
MELBOURNE AND DELHI

For Dorling Kindersley
Senior Editor Elizabeth Dowsett
Managing Art Editor Ron Stobbart
Managing Editor Catherine Saunders
Brand Manager Lisa Lanzarini
Publishing Manager Simon Beecroft
Category Publisher Alex Allan
Production Editor Siu Yin Chan
Production Controller Rita Sinha
Reading Consultant Maureen Fernandes

For Lucasfilm
Executive Editor J. W. Rinzler
Art Director Troy Alders
Keeper of the Holocron Leland Chee
Director of Publishing Carol Roeder

Designed and edited by Tall Tree Ltd
Designer Jonathan Vipond
Editor Jon Richards

First published in Great Britain in 2011 by
Dorling Kindersley Limited
80 Strand, London, WC2R 0RL

A CIP catalogue record for this book
is available from the British Library.

ISBN: 978-1-40535-100-3

Reproduced by Media Development and Printing Ltd., UK
Printed and bound in Slovakia by TBB

Discover more at:
www.dk.com
www.starwars.com

Contents

DK READERS

STAR WARS
CLONE TROOPERS
IN ACTION

Clare Hibbert

What a huge army! These soldiers are clone troopers. Every soldier is the same. The soldiers are human, but they wear armour that makes them look like robots.

The troopers fight
for the Republic.
So do the Jedi.

The Jedi

The Jedi are warriors
who fight for good.
Not all of the Jedi are
human. They are many
different creatures.

Obi-Wan Kenobi was the first
Jedi to see the clone troopers.
He discovered the army on a
planet near the edge of the galaxy.
This planet is called Kamino.

Obi-Wan Kenobi

Obi-Wan Kenobi is a
Jedi Master. A Jedi
Master is a high-
ranking Jedi who has
carried out many brave
acts. Obi-Wan is very
skilled at fighting with
his lightsaber.

This is Jango Fett. He is very good at fighting. All the clone troopers are copies of Jango. Scientists made the clone babies and grew them inside glass jars. The babies will grow into troopers.

Clones

Clones are exact copies of living things. Thousands of clones of Jango Fett have been made to create the clone army.

The clones are off to fight their first battle. They fly to the battle inside huge warships. Jedi Master Yoda flies with them. He is a very wise Jedi. He is hundreds of years old.

Clone troopers wear helmets and tough body armour. The armour covers the troopers' bodies.

The armour is very strong so that it protects the clone troopers in battle.

Officers

Clone officers wear blue, green, red or yellow stripes on their armour. Yellow is for the highest rank – clone commander.

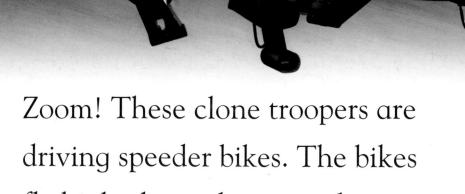

Zoom! These clone troopers are driving speeder bikes. The bikes fly high above the ground.

They are super-fast and are used
to soar above a planet's surface.
The bikes have blaster cannons
to fire at enemies.

This is an even faster way to travel! This starfighter is flown by a clone pilot. Starfighters are small and fast ships. They are often launched from larger ships to attack the enemy.

Clone pilots
Just like the clone troopers, clone pilots are
exact copies of Jango Fett.

Oh no! These clone troopers are attacking a Jedi. What is going on? Chancellor Palpatine has told everyone that the Jedi are bad. He orders the clone troopers to attack the Jedi suddenly so that the Jedi can't fight back.

Evil leader

Chancellor Palpatine is hungry for power. He pretends to be good, but he will stop at nothing to take control of the whole galaxy.

Now the troopers are called stormtroopers. They don't fight with the Jedi. They fight against them. The stormtroopers obey Palpatine and his second-in-command, Darth Vader. Palpatine is now called the Emperor and he rules the galaxy.

Darth Vader

Darth Vader
is part-human
and part-machine.
He was once a Jedi
Knight called Anakin
Skywalker, but now he
has turned to evil.

Some stormtroopers have special jobs. Scout troopers check out enemy territory. Snowtroopers fight on icy worlds. No matter what their job, all stormtroopers are well known for one thing – they always follow orders!

Scout trooper

Snowtrooper

This tall walking tank is called an AT-AT. It carries stormtroopers into battle. They are looking for Princess Leia and the secret Rebel base on an icy planet called Hoth. Quick! Stop those walkers!

Rebels
The Rebel Alliance is fighting against Emperor Palpatine and the stormtroopers. Princess Leia is one of the Rebel commanders.

Stormtroopers are strong, but they are no match for Chewbacca. Get them, Chewie! Wait! These aren't stormtroopers!

Luke and his friend Han Solo are wearing stormtrooper armour as a disguise!

These stormtroopers are on a very large spaceship called the Death Star. They are guarding the Death Star from any Rebel attacks.

Death Star
The Death Star is shaped like an enormous ball. It is powerful enough to destroy an entire planet!

Can Luke, Han and Leia defeat
the stormtroopers and destroy the
Death Star?

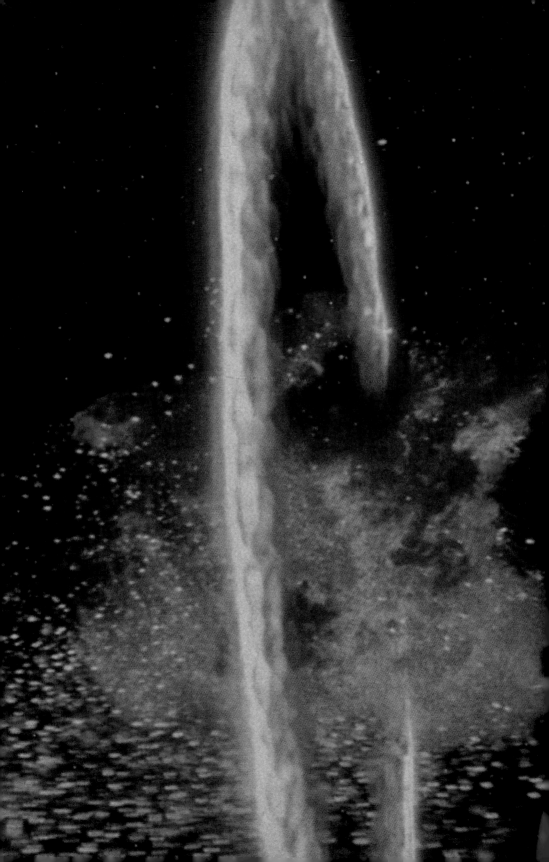

Hurray! Luke and his
friends Han, Chewie and
Leia have helped the Rebels
destroy the Death Star.
But what will happen to the
stormtroopers?
Will they rise again to fight
the valiant Rebels?

Quiz

1. Are clone troopers robots?

2. Who was cloned to make the troopers?

3. Where were the first clone troopers from?

4. What rank is this yellow clone trooper?

5. Who is this Rebel commander ?

6. Who gives orders to the stormtroopers?

Answers: 1. No, they are humans. 2. Jango Fett, a bounty hunter. 3. The planet Kamino. 4. Commander. 5. Princess Leia. 6. Darth Vader and Palpatine.